I.S.B.N. 0-85079-094-8

SUNDAY EXPRESS & DAILY EXPRESS
CARTOONS

Thirty-fourth Series

A DAILY EXPRESS PUBLICATION

£1.20

INTRODUCTION

by

DENIS

NORDEN, C.B.E.

**Script writer,
and well known
Television personality**

Dear Giles,

Breakfast is reckoned to be a highly important meal, if only because so many wives get upset if you're not home by then. For me, however, it comes at a time of day when my bio-rhythms are giving a practically nil reading. That's why the only thing I would ever be prepared to say in its favour is that it brings the daily Giles cartoon. Over the years, his squat and malignant creations have done more to equip me for the day that lies ahead than any of the highly touted mixtures of wheat-chaff and bran.

I'd go further. As I grow older—which I now seem to do with increasing facility—there tend to be more and more mornings when you look through the newspaper and realise that the only credible figure left in British public life is Grandma.

For that reason, there will be those purchasers for whom this bunch of Giles cartoons will represent something of significant social value. If, on the other hand, all you get out of them is a succession of happily malicious giggles, that's probably even more socially valuable.

Especially at breakfast time.

Yours,

Denis Norden

"Hear that, everybody? If some of you don't start enjoying yourselves Father won't bring us again next year."

Sunday Express, August 26th, 1979

"You realise, sir, you are contributing to the 'avalanche of lawlessness threatening to engulf our civilisation.'"

Daily Express, July 5th, 1979

"Stand by! Skylab returning to earth—over."

Sunday Express, July 8th, 1979

"Daddy, I think Mrs Montpelier-Smythe heard you say, thanks to her rock cakes, building may now commence."

Sunday Express, July 15th, 1979

"Son—seems white man has dropped as big a clanger with our oil as he has with the rest of our property."

Daily Express, July 17th, 1979

"No, we can *not* hang Auntie Bertha because she wants to bring back hanging."

Daily Express, July 19th, 1979

"Please take the Colonel's ball back where you found it at once."

Sunday Express, July 22nd, 1979

"Did you see the Wildfowl Trust suggest we all 'adopt a duck' to preserve the species. Can you imagine?"

Daily Express, July 26th, 1979

"Dad—Grandma's just swallowed six thousand eight hundred and seventy-three greenflies."

Sunday Express, July 29th, 1979

"Get it right out of your head about marrying the Queen of England—she's already married."

Sunday Express, August 5th, 1979

"Far enough, Adonis."

Sunday Express, August 12th, 1979

"Her husband knows exactly what he wants—whatever she says he's going to get."

Daily Express, August 14th, 1979

"Right! After that it's Mars Bars for the lot of you."

(Racehorse winner disqualified for eating Mars Bars . . .)

Sunday Express, August 19th, 1979

"Looks like you'll be rejoining us for the old egg, chips, and peas, duckie."

Daily Express, August 21st, 1979

"No ITV and BBC repeat repeats is driving us to drink."

Daily Express, August 23rd, 1979

"This gentleman complains that you flew low over his nudist camp and stuck a parking ticket on him."

Sunday Express, September 2nd, 1979

"I don't care if she did have to pay the fare for her Teddy, I'm not giving it my seat."

Daily Express, September 4th, 1979

"I wish Vicar hadn't read our new Archbishop breeds the wretched things."

Sunday Express, Sept. 9th, 1979

"Which of our Casanovas sent this suggestion that the age of consent should be decided by the Minister of Sport?"

Daily Express, September 13th, 1979

"Yes, I remember well this is where we first discussed the age of consent; you also discussed it with Florrie Finch, Queenie Quinn, and most of the other WAAFs in my outfit."

Daily Express, September 16th, 1979

Daily Express, September 18th, 1979

"Grandma—is this your ad. in the local paper? 'WANTED, Guard dog for now very valuable gold wedding ring'."

Daily Express, September 20th, 1979

"The sooner your mother gets one of these State-supplied baby sitters to look after the rest of her family the better."

Sunday Express, September 23rd, 1979

"Kerridge, is there anything in the book that says I have to take my secretary's damn baby back as well?"

Daily Express, September 27th 1979

"Great for our public image—the nick bunged full of drunk and disorderly birthday revellers."

Sunday Express, September 30th, 1979

"Action stations! Sebastian Coe and Steve Ovett back from lunch."

Daily Express, October 4th, 1979

"I'd like to see Joe Gormley get mine to work one day a week."

(Miners' leader Gormley calls for one-day week for all . . .)

Sunday Express, October 7th. 1979

"Methinks those who are not putting in their reports hath already sold them to the Sunday papers."

Daily Express, October 9th, 1979

"We've got to do something to hold on to the customers in case ITV comes back next week."

Sunday Express, October 14th, 1979

"I tell him the Mini's back and he says: 'Good, did they get rid of that squeak in the offside door?'"

Daily Express, October 18th, 1979

"One small modification of the rules—no one goes over the wall to get their ball back."

Sunday Express, October 21st, 1979

"Here we go—demanding a higher rate for the job now he's got to deliver one more paper."

Daily Express, October 23rd, 1979

"Sir Hugh Casson? About that luxury villa on the Costa Brava you're designing for me—make it two."

Daily Express, October 25th, 1979

"That Head started something sending them home for having short hair—bald as a snooker ball every one of 'em!"

Sunday Express, October 28th, 1979

"It's not often I see eye to eye with chief constables."

Daily Express, October 30th, 1979

"Personally speaking, I'd prefer 'L'Entree at Maxims' to 'Roast lamb and two veg' on British Rail."

(French ban English lamb . . .)

Sunday Express, November 4th, 1979

"This girl Fonteyn could do well if she sticks at it."

Daily Express, November 6th, 1979

"I knew damn well we shouldn't have asked that Aussie taxi driver for the shortest cut to the practice pitch."

Daily Express, November 8th, 1979

"You'd never think he had the reputation of being one of the worst Pig Sergeants of World War Two."

Sunday Express, November 11th, 1979

"Look who is howling her head off over Reggie Bosanquet retiring—the same one who won't let me watch Anna Ford!"

Daily Express, November 13th, 1979

"Hey you. Get this lot out of 'ere."

(Night workers take beds to work . . .)

Daily Express, November 15th, 1979

"Nice of you to come and explain to my missus why you're calling us all out just a few weeks before Christmas, Robbo."

Daily Express, November 22nd, 1979

"From the BBC. Urgent economies. All future safaris on the sex-life of the Lowland Gorilla Flea will journey no further than the London Zoo."

Sunday Express, November 25th, 1979

"As rich Americans can no longer afford our prices, we are compelled to charge water as an optional extra for Room with Bath."

Daily Express, November 27th, 1979

"I heard you say: 'We have ways of keeping you warm, nurse.' What did she say?"

Daily Express, November 29th, 1979

"And if I had the price of the fare I'd fly over and belt her one."

Sunday Express, December 2nd, 1979

"I just heard your boss say he's going to trade you in for a computerised, air-conditioned, articulated tractor."

Daily Express, December 4th, 1979

"I would be more inclined to believe in Father Christmas if I didn't see him leaving for work after his usual ding-dong with his missus."

Daily Express, December 6th, 1979

"Dad, the lady says that's exactly what Prince Philip was on about—making Britain dirty."

Sunday Express, December 9th, 1979

"Hold it, man—we can't go around punching happy shoppers just because they poked their Christmas tree in your eye."

Daily Express, December 11th, 1979

"Introducing Super Glue for the paper chains shows a marked failure to understand the imaginative workings of the modern child's mind, Miss Winslow."

Daily Express, December 13th, 1979

"He was full of it *before* Prince Charles had a ride on him."

Sunday Express, December 16th, 1979

"I love the indignation when it's people in high places. Mine doesn't know I know about his little carry-on with my hairdresser."

Daily Express, December 18th, 1979

"Your Yuletide message to the office party last year, sir? Same as the year before—Merry Christmas, everybody. Over and out."

Daily Express, December 20th, 1979

"Well, he wanted a bike and you wanted a turkey. . . ."

Sunday Express, December 23rd, 1979

"Dad, Mum says would you like a mince pie while we're waiting for the fire brigade?"

Daily Express, December 24th, 1979

"I don't think Auntie Esther meant her present to be worn OVER your topcoat, Dad."

Daily Express, December 27th, 1979

"Just two more days of the Year of the Child then the Year of the Adult takes over in this house."

Sunday Express, December 30th, 1979

"Mirror, mirror on the wall, who's the luckiest of them all? I booked a package holiday to Afghanistan!"

Daily Express, January 4th, 1980

"Everybody up! Decorations down! And I warn you we're not very happy with our wage settlement."

Sunday Express, January 6th, 1980

"Singh says if they send him his papers he'll rejoin the Bengal Lancers in a flash."

Daily Express, January 8th, 1980

"Bennett, after diligent research into history, comes up with the illuminating observation that we have gone through 13 Prime Ministers since the birth of Donald Duck."

Daily Express, January 10th, 1980

"I see your old treacherous tribal riff-raff, enemies of the British Raj, are now your glorious allies, Colonel."

Sunday Express, January 13th, 1980

"I can't wait to get out there and play with my Christmas present from your father."

"All this talk about where they're holding the Olympics makes Mercury here a little tired."

Daily Express, January 17th, 1980

"Nurse, you will inform your ward that the new pigeon service is not installed for the passing of betting slips."

Sunday Express, January 20th, 1980

"Sorry, my wife's fitted me up with one of these new bleepers so she knows where I am."

Daily Express, January 22nd, 1980

"Let her make a hundred before we tell her she may have to switch to eagles."

Sunday Express, January 27th, 1980

"If you have all shop stewards beheaded in the Tower, you'll have the executioners out before you can say chop!"

Daily Express, January 29th, 1980

"She certainly looks like the new beer mats, but she's nothing like Mrs Thatcher."

(This odd impression of Margaret Thatcher appeared on beer mats this week)

Daily Express, January 31st, 1980

"I don't think she got the job, Dad."

Sunday Express, February 3rd, 1980

"Penelope, I thought you told me you were a good poker player."

Daily Express, February 5th, 1980

"Someone tell the old fool we're not digging holes outside her house to tap her damn phone."

Daily Express, February 7th, 1980

"We're waiting for a call from Barbara Woodhouse—she said 'SITT-T-T' at Crufts and they won't unsit till she tells them."

Sunday Express, February 10th, 1980

"Like Kennedy Airport banning the Russians—if you don't let 'em in, they can't beat you."

Daily Express, February 12th, 1980

"First thing she's going to do when she's an MP is straighten up the whole world."

Daily Express, February 19th, 1980

"I don't suppose it will affect his judgment although it *was* his parked car you kicked in and one of you broke his son-in-law's nose."

Daily Express, February 21st, 1980

"Know what I'm giving up for Lent? One or two things like Housework, Washing-up, Ironing . . ."

Sunday Express, February 24th, 1980

"Verily I say unto you, if you drop that bleeding spanner on my nut once more . . ."
(Archbishop of York deplores TV violence . . .)

Daily Express, February 26th, 1980

"I know I haven't won £953,874 and 10p—I was just thinking how nice it'd be if I had."

Daily Express, February 28th, 1980

"Vera thinks she's helping the BBC save its £130 million by not switching it on."

Sunday Express, March 2nd, 1980

"Don't spoil it for him—flag made in Japan and shirt made in Hong Kong."

Sunday Express, March 9th, 1980

"Watch it, boy! They expel
us for that sort of lark."

(Students banned for sharing beds)

Daily Express, March 6th, 1980

"I hear they're getting higher pay than we are."

Daily Express, March 11th, 1980

"I gather the seeds you sowed yesterday for Mother's Day flowers didn't come to much."

Sunday Express, March 16th, 1980

"No, it WILL NOT be one way of raising our fare to the Olympics!"

Daily Express, March 18th, 1980

"Eternal stink of after shave! Ever since we've had a woman station manager."

Daily Express, March 20th, 1980

"It's a shame her making him wear that—he doesn't even watch Dallas."

Sunday Express, March 23rd, 1980

"Once it was: 'You've never had it so good,' now it's: 'You've had it worse,' tomorrow it'll probably be: 'You've had it!'"

Daily Express, March 25th, 1980

"I doubt if making Fifi eat outside on her own will bring the French to heel."

Daily Express, March 27th, 1980

"The BBC has banned players advertising and so have I!"

Sunday Express, March 30th, 1980

"Joke cigars for April Fool's Day prompt me to suggest you're long overdue for retirement, Hennesey."

Daily Express, April 1st, 1980

"How come it's all right for Brighton, but in Eastbourne you end up in the nick?"

Daily Express, April 3rd, 1980

"Finish making Grandma's Easter egg later and tell her breakfast is ready."

Sunday Express, April 6th, 1980

"If any of them shouted at me like they shouted at the Minister of Education I'd annihilate 'em."

Daily Express, April 10th, 1980

"Not bad—could do with a few beheadings and floggings to liven it up."

Sunday Express, April 13th, 1980

"The Manager says Natwest can't afford to sponsor cricket for £1½ million *and* sponsor a new roof on our clubhouse."

Daily Express, April 17th, 1980

"For doing that I want you to know that my feelings about Mark Phillips v the horse are not entirely with the horse."

Sunday Express, April 20th, 1980

"In my day, Annabel, presented at court didn't mean for doing a ton, taking a trip, or busting the fuzz . . ."

Daily Express, April 22nd, 1980

"Why has father started joining us for lunch, ma?"

Daily Express, April 24th, 1980

"Oh dear, now we really are on the brink of World War 3—he's out first ball of the season."

Sunday Express, April 27th, 1980

"I wouldn't get up yet—Grandma's still sounding off about paying £2 million transfer fees with her money."

Sunday Express, May 4th, 1980

"Message from H.Q.: 'All S.A.S. men will enter by the back door.'"

Daily Express, May 8th, 1980

"I expect they threatened to stop a day's pay."

(Leader of the T.U.C. recalled from holiday for Action Day . . .)

Daily Express, May 13th, 1980

"So far she hasn't joined the chorus of witty jokes about inflation."

Sunday Express, May 18th, 1980

"I suppose this means peace could break out anywhere without us knowing a thing about it."

Daily Express, May 20th, 1980

"So sorry, Mrs. Cholmondley, nurse is a little niggly about the disparity in our salaries."

Daily Express, May 22nd, 1980

"Robert is so against sending athletes to Moscow on principle, I wish he would apply his principles to St. Botolph's Fete."

Sunday Express, May 25th, 1980

"Fiver Terry Wogan, because if he isn't on the Dallas show it's the only one he ain't."

Daily Express, May 27th, 1980

"Just in case we find 500 coppers lined up at each end of Downing Street."

Daily Express, May 29th, 1980

"You're not to keep calling your cousin Charles a blackleg."

"I suppose you can even remember what they had before Coronation Street, Grandma?"

Daily Express, June 3rd, 1980

"When my old man was a cop, he'd have handled this with a clip over
the ear and a warning that next time he'd tell their dad."
(Pictures of future police uniforms were published today . . .)

Daily Express, June 5th, 1980

"You can stop coming to work in disguise, Doctor, we have decided on non-belligerent action."

Sunday Express, June 8th, 1980

"You should get a splendid view of Trooping The Colour from there,
madam—you're on the exact spot where Her Majesty will be taking the salute."

Daily Express, June 12th, 1980

"I'm not coming down to the beach with you in that!"

Sunday Express, June 15th, 1980

"I can see the headline for my memoirs: 'How I quelled the fans in the Strawberry Teas enclosure'."

Daily Express, June 17th, 1980

"But Prince Charles slid off to play polo before the end of the first race, Mama."

Daily Express, June 19th, 1980

"Geraldine, I thought you were coming to the 'Ban the U.S. Nuclear Cruise Missiles' meeting!"

Sunday Express, June 22nd, 1980

"OK! So I had six Heads of State on board at the same time so I mista the chance!"

Daily Express, June 24th, 1980

"Good news—instead of progress, we're going backwards!"

Daily Express, June 26th, 1980

"Yes, I saw on TV it's our last chance to save the elephant. Now get it out of the garage."

Daily Express, July 3rd, 1980